Acknowledgments

Special thanks to the West Virginia Division of Highways for its maintenance and care of the New River Gorge Bridge and to New River Gorge National River for its stewardship of the river and land around the bridge.

We extend our appreciation to Charles Ocheltree at the West Virginia Division of Culture and History, the West Virginia State Historic Preservation Office, and Ericka Broyles at the Beckley *Register-Herald* for help with research and photo searches. Engineers Rodney Holbert, P.E. of Burgess and Niple, Inc. and Jimmy Wriston, P.E. of WV DOT read early versions of the manuscript and provided valuable comments. Benjy Simpson of Bridge Walk also offered help and support of this project. A sincere thank you goes to Martha Opdahl for proofreading these pages and to Ginger Rolling for her valuable assistance as our design specialist.

ISBN 978-1-7322123-0-5

Library of Congress Control Number: 2018941020

Printed in the United States of America
First printing, 2018

122 Goddard Ave.
Fayetteville, WV 25840

Cover photo by Randall Sanger
Photo previous page by Bruce Burgin

The New River Gorge Bridge

A Modern Engineering Marvel

By Cristina Opdahl and William Strasser

Before the Bridge

The story of the New River Gorge Bridge begins with an ancient question: how do I get to the other side of the river? For generations, Native Americans and local peoples feared crossing the dangerous whitewater of the New River, nicknaming it the "River of Death." The steep slopes of the New River Gorge also presented a barrier to early travel.

The development of railroads in West Virginia following the Civil War brought an end to the region's isolation from the outside world. The completion of the Chesapeake and Ohio Railroad in 1873 connected Covington, Virginia, through the New River Gorge with the Ohio River at Huntington, West Virginia, at a cost of some $23 million—over $400 million in today's dollars.

The arrival of the railroad forever changed a sparsely populated land of subsistence farmers into a bustling region of coal mining and timber logging production. From the 1880s through the 1930s, coal mining boomed in southern West Virginia as new immigrants, African Americans from the Deep South, and other workers flocked here for job opportunities. Every half-mile along the river sat a town built by a coal company. These coal towns lined the steep walls of the New River Gorge, and the coal produced here fueled America's burgeoning Industrial Revolution.

The railroad brought with it new connections to the mid-Atlantic United States and beyond, as twenty to thirty passenger and freight trains roared through the New River Gorge each day. Railroad bridges across the New River meant that

Right: At half a mile across and 900 feet deep, the New River Gorge has been an obstacle to travel for millennia.

Before railroads and roads came to the New River Gorge, long, flat-bottomed boats called "batteaux" were the primary way to move commercial goods between upper New River communities.

Although railroads dominated area transportation in those days, they were not the only way to get around. As early as 1790, the state of Virginia built a wagon road that traveled through the New River Gorge near the town of Sewell, using a ferry to cross the river. After the 1873 completion of the railroad, local politicians pushed for increased road access from the railroad to the county seat of Fayetteville. In 1889, the county funded the construction of the Fayette Station Bridge, which still stands near the site of the present-day New River Gorge Bridge.

By the end of World War II in 1945, there were signs that the "boom" times of coal mining in the New River Gorge were beginning to go "bust." Increased mechanization in the coal mines meant that fewer workers were needed to mine coal. Much of the easily reached coal had been mined out over the last fifty years. Blue collar workers left southern West Virginia to find new jobs in Detroit, Cleveland, and other parts of the Rust Belt.

With the decline of the coal industry in Appalachia, national leaders looked for ways to help the region

people could cross the river safely. Many people walked over these bridges to commute to work in the coal mines.

recover and develop economically. Moved by the poverty he saw during campaign trips to West Virginia, President John F. Kennedy formed the President's Appalachian Regional Commission in 1963 and directed it to create a comprehensive program for the economic development of the Appalachian region. Studies quickly showed that a modern highway system was essential for access and economic growth, and the 1965 Appalachian Development Act authorized the Appalachian Development Highway System. Congress appropriated $840 million for construction of highways in the region, including six new highways in West Virginia.

One of these highways was to be a 70-mile link between what is now I-79 near Sutton, WV, and what is now I-77 near Beckley, WV, known to planners as Corridor L and known to us today as Route 19. Corridor L would save travelers over 45 miles of travel. There was only one problem: the New River Gorge.

The mining towns of Kaymoor (at right) and Nuttallburg (at left) were among the dozens of coal towns every half a mile up and down the Gorge during the late 19th and early 20th centuries.

A car winds its way down Fayette Station Road in the early 1900s.

People often say that the construction of the New River Gorge Bridge took the commute across the Gorge from 45 minutes to 45 seconds. This isn't far from the truth. The scenic Fayette Station Road winds through the New River Gorge, allowing visitors to take in views of the river, the gorge, and the New River Gorge Bridge from unique angles. The road, which is primarily one-way, begins on the north side of the gorge near the National Park Service Canyon Rim Visitors Center. Crossing the New River over Fayette Station Bridge is a highlight of the drive. Pedestrian walkways on either side allow visitors to walk out on the bridge and view the New River Gorge Bridge some 800 feet above.

Fayette Station Bridge has a fascinating history of its own. The original, a 279-foot-long truss bridge, was completed in 1889 to omit a dangerous river crossing from the route connecting Fayetteville, the county seat, and the town of South Fayette to Fayette Station, the C&O Railway stop on the north side of the river. Fayette Station Bridge was the first bridge to cross the New River in Fayette County, and the American Bridge Company—the same company that would later build the New River Gorge Bridge—built it.

Fayette Station Road was paved in 1928 and became part of the state road system in 1933. After the completion of the New River Gorge Bridge in 1977, Fayette Station Bridge was closed to traffic and left in a dilapidated state. In 1997, it was rehabilitated and reconstructed, using as many original parts as possible. It reopened to the public in September 1998. The bridge was renamed in honor of Tunney Hunsaker, the long-time Chief of Police in Fayetteville.

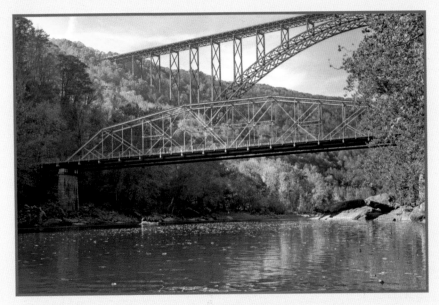

Whitewater rafters pass underneath Fayette Station Bridge before taking out on the left-hand side of the river.

Planning the Bridge

Locals had long pushed for an improved bridge across the New River Gorge. The *Fayette Tribune* argued in September, 1956, that a bridge would "greatly increase present prosperity and act as a guarantee of good times for the future." Increased access to coal fields as well as natural areas like Babcock State Park would help the area develop economically.

But just how do you build a bridge across the New River Gorge, which is over a half mile across and nearly 900 feet deep? A plan to build a four-lane highway descending one side of the Gorge and ascending the other was quickly eliminated as too expensive. That left three bridge options for engineering firm Michael Baker Jr., Inc. to choose from: a suspension bridge, a truss, or a steel arch bridge. Chief Engineer Clarence Knudsen described their decision-making process to the Beckley, WV, *Register and Post-Herald* in October of 1977:

A suspension bridge would have been 2,000 to 3,100 feet long, well within an economical range for such bridges. But this type [of] structure was ruled out, for the bridge towers, which would rise 300 to 350 feet on top of the mountains on each side of the gorge would have posed a hazard for aircraft.

A truss bridge with eight spans was technically feasible. But this scheme was

Right: The design of the bridge required almost 5,000 calculation sheets, and the number of hours of calculations required are equal to one person working 40 hours per week for 15 years.

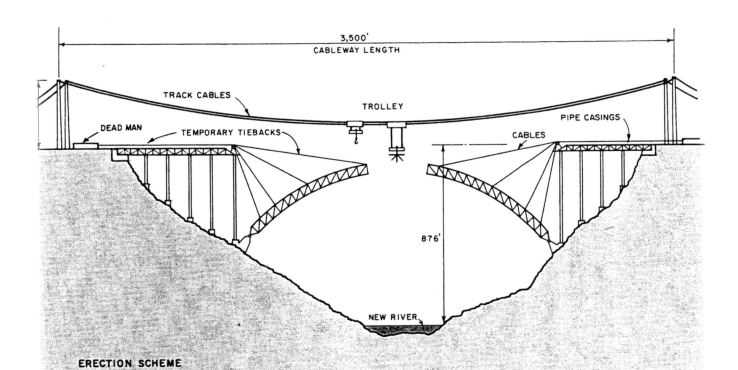

3,500'
CABLEWAY LENGTH

TRACK CABLES

TROLLEY

PIPE CASINGS

DEAD MAN

TEMPORARY TIEBACKS

CABLES

876'

NEW RIVER

ERECTION SCHEME

It appeared that the best solution would be a steel arch bridge. Simple, clean, and symmetrical, a steel arch was the perfect design for the bridge. An arch would blend in with its surroundings rather than stand out and dominate it. Rust-colored COR-TEN steel would help the bridge further blend in with its environment.

Engineers were assisted by 1970s-era computers for the massive number of calculations needed to complete the design. Chief Engineer Knudsen explained in a 1977 article in *Civil Engineering Magazine*:

Today's engineers make use of powerful computers to analyze the stresses in the bridge's members. The computer allows stresses in the arch to be determined much more accurately. The best shape of the arch and the most economical member size can be determined more accurately. Result: much less time needed to do calculations; [and] a considerable savings in steel, since materials are being used more efficiently.

The contract to build the bridge was awarded in June 1973 to the United States Steel Corporation's American Bridge Division. American Bridge beat three other bids to build the bridge with their proposal of $33.9 million dollars (the final cost was $37 million). Large bridge projects were nothing new to American Bridge, having built the previous record-holder for an arch bridge in the 1930s,

New Jersey's Bayonne Bridge. Regardless of price, the New River Gorge Bridge would be the largest West Virginia Department of Highways project to date, with 70 percent of the money provided by the federal government and 30 percent by the state of West Virginia.

Designed by US Steel's American Bridge Division, the Bayonne Bridge in New Jersey was the longest steel arch bridge in the world at the time of its completion in 1931.

The rust color of COR-TEN steel blends well with the New River Gorge.

The New River Gorge Bridge is made of COR-TEN steel, a product of the U.S. Steel Corporation that oxidizes over time and forms its own protective coating of rust on the outside. COR-TEN has two benefits: Because it produces its own protective coating, it was designed to not be painted. The estimated cost of painting the bridge—each time!—was roughly $1 million. The second benefit is aesthetic. The deep russet color of the steel is an earthy color and blends in well with the mountainous terrain.

There was one negative, however: more difficult inspections. The bridge is inspected annually, and each inspection by an army of highly trained professional engineers takes about 3 weeks. From an Inventory Bridge Inspection Report by Michael Baker, Jr. Inc.:

While the use of COR-TEN steel negates the need for painting, routine inspections are more difficult than those for painted steel structures. On a painted steel structure, rust indicates developing paint failure, and fatigue cracks are made evident by the color of paint and the rust along the crack. Since the entire weathering steel bridge is covered with rust, inspectors must have knowledge of different stages of exposure of the oxide film and must examine it using hammers and wire brushes to determine if it adheres to the steel base.

Other interesting facts about the COR-TEN steel used in the bridge include:

- The amount of steel in the bridge would make approximately 15,000 mid-sized automobiles.
- The largest joint in the bridge contains 2,300 bolts.
- The bridge shrinks in cold temperatures. At -10 degrees Fahrenheit, the highest point of the bridge is 10.5 inches lower than it is at 60 degrees F.

Expansion joints (center right) allow the bridge to rock and sway with the wind, heat, and other movement.

Unique Challenges

American Bridge Division began several parts of the project at once, including constructing access roads and filling forms with concrete for bridge pier foundations. A unique challenge in this project was that the steep slopes of the New River Gorge had been mined for coal some fifty years earlier. To insure the foundations would be solid, hundreds of deep borings had to be made. Enormous voids were discovered in two locations critical for the bridge pier foundations. To fill up the holes and stabilize the ground, a sand and concrete mix was inserted through 6-inch holes into the former mines, which created a "cone" that in turn provided a base for the large concrete footings that would support the bridge.

While foundation work continued, fabrication of the steel beams was underway in Ambridge, Pennsylvania, and Gary, Indiana. All major beams were milled to a tolerance of 1/100 of an inch. In a sense, much of the bridge was assembled twice. First, the beams were assembled at the fabrication plant so that their dimensions could be confirmed. They were then taken apart again, transported to the New River Gorge construction site, and re-assembled for installation.

Transporting the massive steel beams and other heavy equipment to the construction site provided yet another challenge. Most of the steel beams were brought in by a railroad that ended 19 miles away in Nallen, West Virginia, and tractor trailers hauled

Right: Construction workers pouring concrete footers for the bridge pier on the north side of the New River Gorge.

Tractor trailers hauled many of the steel beams from the railroad to the construction site.

them the rest of the way to an assembly area on the gorge's north side.

But West Virginia's winding country roads were not adequate to transport the heaviest beams. These were brought in by railroad cars and raised up to the top of the gorge with a cable system.

Beams were stored in the assembly area in sections. Because the cableway could carry up to 100 tons, individual beams could be assembled together into sections on the ground in the assembly yard and transported out to the site as needed by the foreman. It was much easier and safer to assemble the steel sections on the ground, and this saved time and money over assembling the bridge piece-by-piece in the air.

One of the biggest challenges in building the New River Gorge Bridge was, how do you get the steel where it needs to go in a construction zone up to 876 feet in midair? The answer was another bridge, a temporary one (dubbed the "highline" by ironworkers) constructed of two 330-foot steel towers on each side, and four 5,000-foot, half-inch-diameter cables strung between by helicopters. As additional cables were attached, each of the four were made as large as 3 inches in diameter, with each cable weighing 30 tons and composed of 294 steel wires. If laid end to end, these would reach a length of 22 miles.

Two diesel-powered trolleys mounted on these cables—and run by two operators in contact with the foreman via radio—made thousands of deliveries and assemblies of the massive steel beams over the three-year project. These trolleys also carried the ironworkers out to their work site. Each trolley could lift 50 tons. Working together, the pair could lift 100 tons, which was significant as several bridge sections weighed 92 tons.

Safety belts connected iron workers to the steel beams during construction.

Ironworkers came from all over West Virginia and all over the country to build the New River Gorge Bridge. Many ironworkers traveled from one large project to the next large project; many came to the New River Gorge due to the height of the project. All were hired through the Charleston office (Local 301) of the International Association of Bridge, Structural, Ornamental and Reinforcing Iron Workers.

Many of the local ironworkers were young, in their early twenties. Ironworker Rusty Wines was afraid of heights when he began the job. A patient foreman let him build up his confidence as he got farther and further out on the catwalk each week until he could finally work at the dizzying heights needed to complete the bridge. What kind of work did the ironworkers do? Some worked as "punks," making up bolts for the bolt-up gang, and others in the bolt-up gang positioned the steel, then pinned and bolted it together.

Despite being milled to 1/100 of an inch, the steel the ironworkers worked with was not necessarily perfect, for it could be damaged in shipment. Ironworker Spud Chandler recalled that they spent a lot of time using sledge hammers to drive pins through the iron to get the holes lined up.

Construction was halted when cold, wet, or windy conditions made the work unsafe, but otherwise, the work went on year-round. Ironworkers recalled that the work was rough in the cold of winter. The wind could blow a work platform 20 feet or more away from the steel, creating a scary situation. The work could also be blistering hot as the iron heated up in the sun. Iron expands as temperatures get hotter, and workers reported hearing strange popping noises as the iron expanded.

Safety measures included temporary handrails, ladders, chain link fences, and safety belts that connected the ironworkers to the steel beams. Two portable "flying carpets" also supported safety nets underneath the workers. But ironworkers reported constant minor injuries, including busted knuckles and fingers, hearing damage, and eye and skin injuries from flying metal shavings. They also described the physical exhaustion of the job, often not being able to eat for hours after arriving home due to the anxiety of the work.

Despite the safety precautions, disaster struck in May 1974 when a temporary platform shifted and several crew members fell, injuring seven men and killing Dan Snodgrass of Malden, West Virginia. Projections indicated that six men would die during the construction, but Mr. Snodgrass was the only construction member to lose his life during the construction of the bridge.

Construction Underway

When the first structural steel was erected in June 1974, construction would continue over the next two-and-a-half years in much the same manner. Steel beams were assembled on solid ground, then transported out to where they were needed on the bridge via the trolley system. Position, pin, and bolt; position, pin, and bolt again became the routine for ironworkers as they assembled the bridge piece-by-piece like a giant Erector Set.

Vertical steel support columns, or towers, were first built atop the concrete foundations, as the floor truss spans (for the base of the roadway) were built at the same time outwards from the sides of the gorge. Construction of the arch itself began in July 1974.

Under normal conditions, arches provide no great problems to bridge builders. But in the New River Gorge, how can you support the arch while it is being assembled in the air from each side? Several options were considered, including temporary supporting towers, but the gorge was too deep to make this practical. The answer was with a massive tieback system (similar to giant fishing rods) constructed to hold the arch in place. Constant support of the arch was provided by oil well casings and almost 10 miles of cables tied off to reinforced concrete foundations known as "dead men."

As the steel arch reached farther into the gorge, the tieback system moved with the arch arms. The

Right: The arch nears completion in early 1976. Note the towers on the far left, the cables suspended in air as part of the trolley system, and the cables holding the arch arms in place as part of the "tieback" system.

overhead cableway lowered the steel sections to the work site, and ironworkers positioned, pinned and bolted each section into place. To the untrained eye, the unfinished arches looked dangerous, as columnist Bob Wills reported in the October 23, 1977 edition of the *Beckley Post-Herald:*

> *When I first saw the bridge [being built] a couple of years or so ago, I couldn't see any way on God's Green Earth for it to be anything other than a disaster. Of course, at that time the bridge was just two parts of an arch stretching out toward each other from opposite sides of the gorge, and from a view underneath on Rt. 82 I could swear I could see the two ends of the soon-to-be-joined arch swaying in the breeze.*

But ironworkers continued to pin and bolt the arch sections out into the gorge. The only disruption to this routine came in March of 1975 when two of the trolley towers collapsed due to a failure in the braking system.

On that day, ironworker Rusty Wines was working on the bolt-up gang 200 feet from the Fayetteville side:

> *All of a sudden you could hear cable running…. I look up toward the towers on the Fayetteville side and the bottom 60 feet was in slow motion collapsing to the ground like it was melting. Those 3 inch cables [were] getting closer and closer, and you knew they were going to come down and cut you up, take the bridge down, and you knew the end was coming.*
>
> *About that time, out in the woods, one of the guy cables breaks loose, and that allowed one of the towers to then fall to the east out into the woods. The next thing I turned to look at down below…they were setting a 100-foot tall, 60-ton tower*

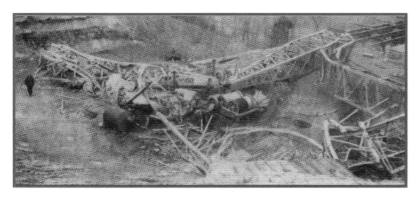

Wreckage from the March 1975 tower collapse. Note the figure at the far left for scale.

stops and it quits moving…. Then I turned and looked toward the Ansted side. The two towers on that side looked like they were free falling toward the side of the bank that had all the trailers where American Bridge had all of their engineers and office people. It fell as far as it could until the lufting cables held and [the cables] stopped it from falling. Once again, another miracle.

leg. Thank God they had enough nuts and bolts in it to hold it together…and ultimately everybody survived that.

The next place I looked was back towards the cables out in the woods. You could see that all that slack now was pulling back through the woods, and there was trees 80 to 100 feet tall just getting chopped down like toothpicks. All of a sudden it just

One of the foremen had parked their truck at the bottom of those towers, and they had crushed [the truck]. Before we could get off the bridge, that truck caught on fire, and it must have had two boxes of shotgun shells in it, because the shotgun shells went off for 20 to 30 minutes.

I truly call it a miracle. It's just one of those great things to live through.

The arms of the arch were held in place by a massive "tieback" system using nearly 10 miles of cable.

It only took three months to build new towers and begin construction again, but this accident contributed to a delay in completion of the project. Initially estimated for fall 1976, project managers pushed the completion target back to the fall of 1977.

By the spring of 1976, the final steel beam of the arch was ready to lay in place. On most bridges, a complicated jacking maneuver would be required to jack the bridge up before placing the last section. For the New River Gorge Bridge, engineers devised a clever solution. They designed the arms slightly too high, and then used the tiebacks or "fishing rods" to lower the arms into place.

On the day scheduled to connect the arms together into one large arch, as the day heated up, the iron started expanding and workers on both sides heard big cracks and saw the arms start swaying 2 to 3 feet or more. Rusty Wines was in the bolt-up gang when the final section was attached, and the tiebacks lowered the arch into its final position. He remembered: "Everything turned out great. It was a great day that day."

With the arch completed, arch towers had to be placed on top of the arch, which would support the future decking for the roadway. The towers were placed symmetrically from the center line to maintain equal weight distribution. Once the towers were complete in June 1976, all that remained was to complete the decking trusses that would support the concrete roadbed above. The final 26-ton deck truss was lowered into place on November 1, 1976, with a ceremony flying US bicentennial and state flags, and an evergreen tree in what is known as a "topping out" ceremony.

Over the remaining months of the project, workers dismantled the towers and tieback system and began construction on the roadway itself. The concrete in

The final placement of steel connecting the two arms in May 1976. To place the final steel beam in the arch, engineers designed the arch arms slightly too high, then placed the beam and lowered the arms into place using the tieback system.

the roadbed had to do more than just serve as the highway. It also had to serve as a counterweight to offset the high winds in the gorge and the traffic along the road. Thousands of tons of concrete and reinforcing steel ultimately went into the roadbed, forming a reinforced concrete slab 8¼ inches thick. A concrete parapet barrier and rails along each side finished off the bridge itself.

Left and opposite page: Ironworkers often celebrate the final piece of steel on a structure with a "topping out" ceremony, signifying that the structure has reached its maximum height. An American flag and a Christmas tree often adorn the final piece of steel, symbolizing good luck and hope that the structure will be everlasting.

Facts and Figures

- **HEIGHT (TO ROAD BASE):** 876 feet, 267 meters
- **BRIDGE LENGTH:** 3030 feet, 923 meters
- **ARCH LENGTH:** 1700 feet, 518 meters
- **RISE OF ARCH:** 360 feet, 109 meters
- **DECK WIDTH:** 69 feet, 21 meters
- **TOTAL WEIGHT:** 88 million pounds, 39.9 million kg
- **WEIGHT OF STEEL:** 44 million pounds, 19.9 million kilograms
- **WEIGHT OF CONCRETE:** 44 million pounds, 19.9 million kilograms
- **SINGLE HEAVIEST STEEL BEAM LIFTED INTO THE ARCH:** 184,000 pounds, 83,460 kilograms
- **WEIGHT OF THE ARCH:** 21,066,000 pounds, 9,555,377 kilograms

Grand Opening

Saturday, October 22, 1977, is known as the official opening day of the New River Gorge Bridge. Some spectators camped out overnight; others arrived at 5 AM, and license plates were observed from more than 11 states and Ontario.

A little-known fact about that first bridge celebration is that the first cars to drive across the bridge did not do so on its opening day. The bridge was temporarily opened the prior weekend because of heavy traffic expected for the opening of hunting season. West Virginia governor Jay Rockefeller ordered the bridge open at noon on Friday, October 14, 1977. It was closed that Sunday at midnight and remained closed until the official opening celebration on the following Saturday.

Right: Five different high school bands played on Opening Day.

On opening day, a mobile post office was set up on the bridge to mark postcards and letters "New River Gorge Bridge," and more than 10,000 special issue stamps were sold. Five area high school bands played. The West Virginia State Amateur Radio Council set up three ham radios so that people could send out messages to friends and relatives from the bridge for free.

Columnist Gene Woodrum wrote in the next day's *Post-Herald* of Beckley:

Old people came, young people, middle aged—people from all walks of life, in both good and bad health. They came on bicycles,

Dignitaries stand at the opening ceremony. From left to right: Governors Okey Patteson, Arch Moore, and Hulett Smith; Oak Hill Mayor J. Walter Brown; Fayette County Delegate Paul McKown; Governor Jay Rockefeller; and Senator Jennings Randolph.

At noon, a ceremony began with Country Music Hall of Famer Charlie McCoy playing the National Anthem on a harmonica. Three former West Virginia governors—Moore, Smith, and Patteson—were present along with current governor Jay Rockefeller, U.S. Senators Jennings Randolph and Robert C. Byrd, and Representative Harley Staggers. Speeches from local and national dignitaries hailed the bridge's engineering significance and future economic impact on the area.

After the ceremony, Governor Jay Rockefeller cut the ribbon to declare the bridge open. He then drove

some in limousines, some in wheelchairs, some in strollers. Some came leading horses, some leading dogs, beagles, poodles, an afghan hound, a collie pup. I felt remiss for not bringing my blue tick coon hound along.

across the bridge in a convertible with his wife Sharon and Tom Wood, the winner of the Charleston Daily Mail's essay contest "Join Jay on the Bridge." Wood, of Fayetteville, won the contest with an essay about his ancestor, Abraham Wood, who was one of the first European explorers of the New River. Gene Woodrum's description of the colorful celebration continues:

> Everything was being sold. I didn't realize that hucksters would have such a field day…. There were bumper stickers, T-shirts, posters, patches, hats, pictures and postcards—even the U.S. mail service had to get in on the great rip-off. We couldn't resist that. We bought 10 stamped envelopes ourselves.

The day after the ceremony, Beckley area newspapers described the dedication as "an event of great moment to a lot of people. It is rather like

Governor Jay Rockefeller cuts the ribbon as essay contest winner Tom Wood looks on.

driving the golden spike that linked East and West by railroad in the 1870s." The newspaper went on to add that the region was "bound to grow, bound to flourish, bound to join together the residents of Southern West Virginia" thanks to the New River Gorge

Bridge. The opening of the bridge did indeed have an immediate impact. Area hospitals noted an increase in

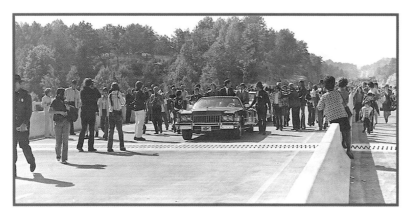

Governor Rockefeller crosses the bridge on Opening Day.

patients, who could get to nearby hospitals much more quickly. Trucking companies reported savings in fuel thanks to the new transportation improvement. Other area businesses saw an increase in traffic and sales.

At the opening of the New River Gorge Bridge, former governor Arch Moore commented that another generation will have to pass before West Virginia realizes the full importance of the New River Gorge Bridge. Indeed, much of the bridge's impact was longer-term. With the new ease in getting to the New River Gorge, tourism in southern West Virginia took off, and local whitewater outfitters flourished in the 1980s and 1990s. Raleigh County's population increased by 24% between 1970 and 1980, and Fayetteville's increased by 38% over the same period, an increase due at least in part to the new bridge. An economic impact study of Corridor L (Route 19) indicates that over 42,000 area jobs exist today that would not exist without the highway system, and those jobs have led to increased wages and made the area more competitive.

Locals and engineering fans alike came out to watch the bridge being built. Upon completion, the bridge became a major tourist attraction. New River Gorge National River, a unit of the National Park Service, was established in 1978 and owns much of the land around the New River Gorge Bridge.

In 1991, the National Park Service opened Canyon Rim Visitor Center overlooking the New River Gorge. Boardwalks from the visitor center lead down to the best views of the bridge. Park rangers share with visitors how to drive Fayette Station Road and get better views of the bridge from underneath.

Canyon Rim Visitor Center at New River Gorge National River is the best place to view and learn about the bridge.

The New River is among the oldest rivers in the world. Flowing northward through the deep canyons of the New River Gorge, it meets up with the Gauley River to form the Kanawha River, and eventually joins the Ohio and Mississippi rivers. In this photo taken from the Canyon Rim Visitor Center overlook, Fayette Station Bridge is just out of view at the bottom of the photo.

Bridge Day®

The New River Gorge Bridge opened on October 22, 1977, but the first Bridge Day was held on November 8, 1980. On that day, two parachute jumpers leapt from a plane and landed on the bridge, and five more parachutists jumped from the bridge. More than 5,000 people earned certificates for walking all the way across the bridge.

The next year, 28 rappellers joined in the Bridge Day fun, rappelling from the catwalk to the bottom of the gorge. By 1984, 300 BASE jumpers leapt from the 876-foot tall span. The 1990s saw bungee jumping added to the Bridge Day festivities, and in 1992 Chris Allum set the world's record for the longest bungee jump from a fixed structure when he jumped from the bridge. Bungee jumping was eventually eliminated from Bridge Day due to safety reasons.

BASE jumping has become a key component of Bridge Day, and BASE jumpers from all over the world know about and come out for the annual event. BASE jumping is parachuting from a fixed structure and stands for "bridge, antenna, span, and earth," the different types of structures from which one jumps. Bridge Day is one of the few times and places in the country where BASE jumping is legal, and the event is especially valued by BASE newcomers who can jump with safety procedures in place.

Right: One of the most unique places to experience Bridge Day is from river level at Fayette Station, where one can look up and watch BASE jumpers come in for a landing.

A "high line"—a controlled zip line with a belay setup—was added to the Bridge Day festivities in 2002. Traditionally held every year on the third Saturday in October, Bridge Day continues to attract both those in search of an adrenaline rush and those content to experience the thrills from the side of the bridge.

300 to 400 jumpers usually come to each Bridge Day. Each jumper typically makes several jumps during the day.

Bridge Day BASE jumpers generally have two to four seconds of free fall before deploying their parachute. They can choose to jump from a platform, a diving board, or even a catapult.

Above: Bridge Day rappellers ascend and/or descend over 700 feet on fixed ropes attached to the bridge.

Right: Rescue boats are always standing by to pull BASE jumpers from the New River.

Opposite page: From pepperoni rolls, funnel cakes, and chili to yard art, jewelry, and t-shirts, visitors can find a little bit of everything available for sale on Bridge Day.

The morning that they opened the bridge was phenomenal. We crested over the hill in Fayetteville at just about daylight and in front of us was thousands of people—we had expected a goodly turnout, but not 25,000 people, and that's what it was. It was a typical October day, the most beautiful foliage you could ask for, and it left you speechless.

—Doug Maddy, first Bridge Day chairman

Maintaining the Bridge

As difficult as building the bridge was, the work was not finished in October, 1977. Once they are built, bridges have to be maintained, and they require regular inspections and maintenance specific to their own needs. In an interview with the author, WVDOT Special Programs Manager Jimmy Wriston said that the greatest inspection challenge on the New River Gorge Bridge comes from rigging and access. Each element of the bridge has to be touched by an inspector. Much of the job can be done with rappel lines and "snooper" trucks hanging over the side, but someone (often the most junior member of the team) has to go down to the bottom of the gorge and climb the internal ladders to examine each piece of the steel.

One unexpected issue that inspections discovered about ten years after the bridge was completed involved the use of rock salt to treat winter roads. Excessive rusting revealed that rock salt was damaging the bridge structure, and a replacement was needed to prevent further damage. The replacement, calcium magnesium acetate (CMA), is not corrosive to the bridge, has a lower freezing point, and is environmentally friendly...and it costs more than 10 times as much as ordinary rock salt. A buffer zone was set up to spread the CMA from Fayetteville to a half-mile north of the bridge, and the new product was found to be very effective. The higher cost of CMA is just part of the cost to preserve the New River Gorge Bridge for the long term.

Right: A snow plow on the bridge creates a unique winter scene, as viewed from Canyon Rim Visitor Center overlook.

Other regular inspections replace bolts, which can rust away over time; the DOH might replace 700 to 800 bolts in a single project. Drains have to be regularly cleaned out and flushed to insure water from the roadway drains down into the gorge properly.

Pigeons are also a big problem for bridges due to the acidic remains they leave behind; pressure washing is necessary to remove these substances and insure that the metal is not corroded. Pigeons have become less of a problem lately due to the reintroduction of peregrine falcons into the New River Gorge. Peregrines like to eat pigeons, and visitors on Bridge Walk tours always enjoy spotting them.

Above and opposite page: Bridge engineers wear special harnesses for safety during inspections.

Someone has to go down to the bottom of the gorge, climb the internal ladders, and touch each piece of the steel.
—Jimmy Wriston

BRIDGE WALK

Driving is not the only way to cross the New River Gorge Bridge. Directly underneath the roadway is a catwalk built into the bridge to provide access to the bridge's underside for inspectors and maintenance crews. Access to the catwalk was off-limits for many years, but many locals tell stories of walking out on the catwalk illegally in their high school days.

For years, locals knew about the catwalk and wanted to create a tour underneath the bridge, similar to that of the Bridge Climb of the Sydney Harbour Bridge in Sydney, Australia—a very popular tourist attraction. It took cooperation between the West Virginia Division of Highways, which owns the bridge—and the National Park Service, which owns much of the land surrounding the bridge—and in 2009, Bridge Walk was founded to give unique tours of the bridge. Visitors on the

Bridge Walk are harnessed and fastened to a safety cable above the catwalk, making it impossible to fall from the bridge during a tour.

WV DOT engineer Jimmy Wriston described the unique experience in the documentary "Iron Men of the Gorge":

> The bridge can move around a lot, [but] the movement is a good thing. *The* bridge weighs 88 million pounds. If it didn't move, it would shake itself apart. It is alive, it breathes, it moves, it lives. It can move longitudinally with temperature. [It] grows and contracts with temperature by a significant degree, has significant wind load, and can move as much as 4 feet laterally due to heavy winds. It vibrates from traffic on top and vibrates from railroad traffic underneath.

The National Park Service reintroduced peregrine falcons to the New River Gorge in the early 2000s. The falcons had an unexpected side benefit for bridge engineers: they ate pigeons nesting on the bridge, thereby reducing acidic pigeon droppings that can damage the steel bridge. Peregrine falcons are sometimes spotted on Bridge Walk tours.

Recognition

Praise from professionals came to the New River Gorge Bridge immediately upon completion. Honors included prizes from the National Steel Bridge Alliance, the National Society of Professional Engineers, and the American Society of Civil Engineers. It is often still named in top-ten lists of all-time bridges.

On October 14, 2005, the US Mint unveiled the official West Virginia State Quarter with a design of the New River Gorge Bridge. More than 1800 design concepts were submitted from around the state. After the entries were narrowed down to five designs, Governor Joe Manchin selected the final design. Designed and engraved by John Mercanti, more than 721 million of the quarters were produced.

On April 11, 2011, the United States Postal Service introduced a $4.95 Priority Mail stamp with a design of the New River Gorge Bridge. Digitally illustrated by Dan Cosgrove and designed by Carl Herrman, the stamp depicts the bridge near sunset. It was seventh in a series of "Wonders of America," and was chosen after being narrowed down from a field of more than 50,000 entries.

In 2013, at the young age of 36, the New River Gorge Bridge was placed on the National Register of Historic Places. For a structure younger than fifty years old to receive this honor, it must demonstrate that it is has "exceptional significance." The New River Gorge Bridge certainly meets that criterion.

Right: At 876 feet above the New River, the New River Gorge Bridge is the third highest bridge in the United States.

Conclusion

In 1975, American Bridge President J.J. Long remarked to the Fayette County Chamber of Commerce: "I can promise you that you will be proud of your bridge, and in my view, this project will later be honored as one of the great engineering construction feats of this century." Today, tourists and locals alike are still captivated by the beauty of the New River Gorge Bridge. What makes it still so appealing all these years later?

In a video made shortly after the completion of the bridge, US Steel highlighted the majestic structure's "ecology, economy, efficiency, and esthetics." In looking back, it is remarkable how well all of these elements came together—the ecology of saving as much of the natural environment as possible; the economy of building the bridge in such a short amount of time; the efficiency of using a simple design and simple materials; and the esthetics of a simple arch to span an ancient, beautiful gorge.

In the same video, US Steel said that history should record that the people charged with building the bridge who found the magnificent gorge left it pretty much as it was. Indeed, the design of the bridge insured that the beauty of the gorge, and the bridge within it, would remain timeless. We hope that the beauty of the New River Gorge and the New River Gorge Bridge may remain an inspiration to future generations.

Right: The New River Gorge Bridge at sunset as seen from Fayette Station Bridge.

For Further Reading

» Historic American Engineering Record, HAER Number WV-60. "Fayette Station Bridge."

» *Iron Men of the Gorge* (video). GMProductions, 2014. *https://www.facebook.com/GMProductionswv/*.

» "New River Gorge Bridge—History." Bridge Walk. *http://bridgewalk.com/history-of-the-bridge.html*.

» "New River Gorge Bridge." National Park Service. *https://www.nps.gov/neri/planyourvisit/nrgbridge.htm*.

» Official Bridge Day Information. *www.officialbridgeday.com*.

» Riebe, Erin. National Register of Historic Places registration form "New River Gorge Bridge," May 2013. *www.wvculture.org/shpo/nr/pdf/fayette/13000603.pdf*.

» United States Steel. *New Records at New River* (video). A Mode-Art Pictures production, 1981.

» Wallace, David Rains. *The New River Gorge: A Corridor in Time*. Eastern National, 2013.

Photo Credits